When I Grow Up
(In Thailand)

For Jupe, Joey and Joss

First printed by Sirivatana Interprint Public Co. Ltd.,
Bangkok Thailand, 2003
This edition 2006

Sirivatana Interprint Company Limited
Thailand

When I Grow Up
(In Thailand)

Janice Santikarn
Illustrated by Sasawat Kayaroj

TUK-TUK DRIVER

When I grow up I'll drive a tuk-tuk,
On Bangkok's busy roads,
I'll pick up groups of tourists,
And pull their heavy loads.

I'll zoom out in the traffic,
Weaving in and out,
And fly around sharp corners,
And rock them all about.

We'll race down tiny Sois,
With room for just one car,
And squeeze by noodle stands,
Without a scratch or scar.

We'll drive by golden temples,
And all the river sights,
And stop to do some shopping,
In the market place at night.

It would be nice to drive a tuk-tuk,
Around Bangkok all day,
But there are too many roads,
And I might lose my way.

ELEPHANT TRAINER

When I grow up I'll train an elephant,
Big and fat and grey,
With floppy ears and swinging trunk,
I'll ride him every day.

I'll teach him how to wave hello,
And how to shake your hand,
To balance on one leg,
And play music in a band.

I'll show him how to kick a ball,
And how to score a goal,
How to paint a picture,
And dance the rock-and-roll.

I'll take good care of him,
I'll bath him every day,
I'll feed him on bananas,
And make a bed of hay.

I'd like to train an elephant,
I think it would be good,
But I'd use up all my money,
Buying tons of food.

PILOT

When I grow up I'll be a pilot,
And fly a big white jet,
Soaring over Thailand,
From Chiang Mai to Phuket.

I'll fly across the mountain tops,
Where hill-tribe people stay,
And leave a trail of smoke behind,
As I go on my way.

Then I'll soar above the clouds,
And race off to Bangkok,
To practice doing loop-the-loops,
Around the temple tops.

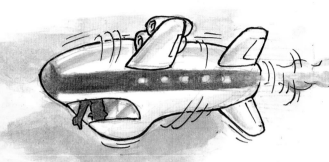

And I'll zoom down to the beach,
At twice the speed of sound,
The swimmers there will stop and stare,
As I fly upside down.

Oh, I'd love to be a pilot,
But I'm rather scared of heights,
Perhaps I'll just stay on the ground,
And learn to fly a kite.

FRUIT SELLER

When I grow up I'll sell fruit,
I'll have a 3-wheel bike,
And pedal all around the streets,
Anywhere I like.

I'll ride into your Soi,
And I'll ring my little bell,
Just to let you know,
I'm there with fruit to sell.

I'll have a box to hold my fruit,
The tastiest you've seen,
Bright green mangoes,
And purple mangosteen.

I'll sell the smelly durian,
And hairy rambutans,
My fruit will be much fresher,
Than what you buy in cans.

Yes, I'd like to sell Thai fruit,
I think it would be fun,
But I'd get all hot and sweaty,
Out in the midday sun.

MONK

When I grow up I'll be a monk,
And shave off all my hair,
I'll wear an orange robe,
And I'll never drink or swear.

I'll wake up very early,
And walk along the streets,
I'll carry a black bowl,
And beg for food to eat.

I'll live inside a temple,
Very plain and bare,
And sit cross-legged on the floor,
To say my daily prayers.

Sometimes I'll be invited,
To bless a brand new plane,
I'll say a special prayer,
So it flies safely home again.

Oh, I'd really like to be a monk,
When I'm grown up and old,
But in the winter months,
My ears would get too cold.

FARMER

When I grow up I'll be a farmer,
With a piece of land,
I'll grow a crop of rice,
And plant it all by hand.

I'll stand in muddy water,
And bend my back down low,
Pushing seeds into the ground,
Row by row by row.

And when the rice plants grow,
Just about knee high,
I'll harvest all the grains,
And lay them out to dry.

Then I'll load the rice,
High upon my cart,
And take it to the market,
To sell for lots of Baht.

It would be great to be a farmer,
Out among the fields and trees,
But I'd never get to go,
A-swimming in the sea.

POLICEMAN

When I grow up, I'll be a policeman,
In a tight brown suit,
With a cap upon my head,
And a badge and shiny boots.

I'll stand out in the busy street,
With traffic whizzing by,
And when I want the cars to stop,
I'll raise my hand up high.

And I will guard the King,
To make sure he's all right,
I'll drive my car in front of his,
And flash red warning lights.

I'll walk the streets at night,
I'll guard your homes and cars,
And if I catch a thief,
I'll throw him behind bars.

But a policeman in Bangkok,
Wouldn't be much fun,
I'd have to wear a mask,
To keep the dust out of my lungs.

THAI DANCER

When I grow up I'll be a dancer,
Dressed in gold and red,
With bracelets on my arms,
And a pointy hat upon my head.

I'll wear an ugly mask,
With fangs and a face of green,
I'll be the strangest creature,
That you have ever seen.

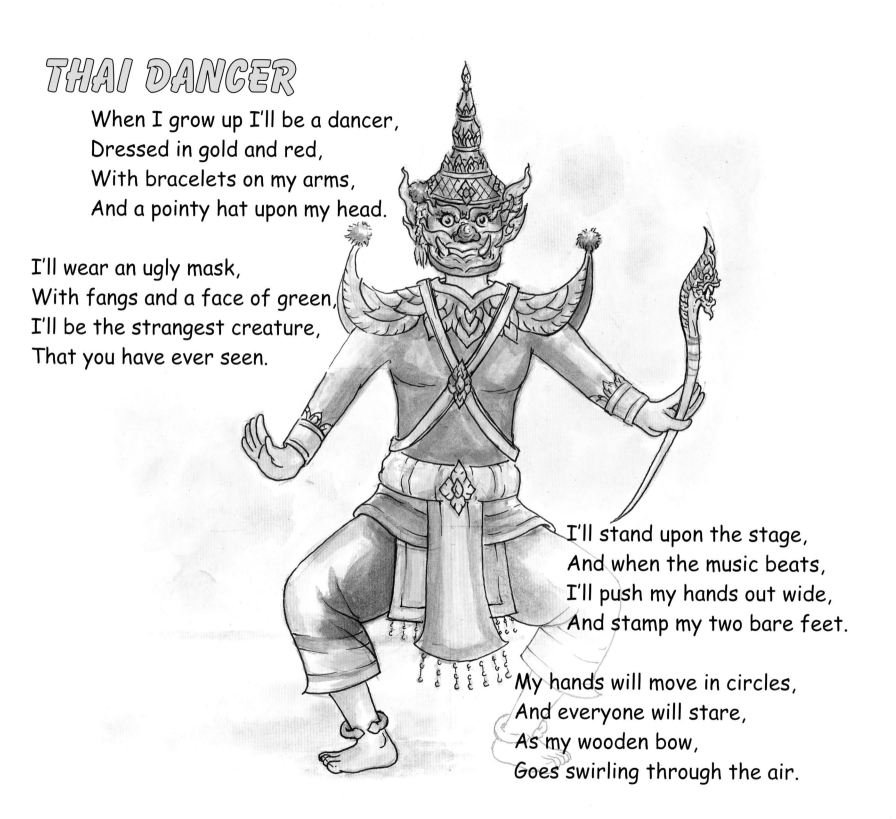

I'll stand upon the stage,
And when the music beats,
I'll push my hands out wide,
And stamp my two bare feet.

My hands will move in circles,
And everyone will stare,
As my wooden bow,
Goes swirling through the air.

It would be fun to be a dancer,
But I'd be dressed up like a doll,
I'd rather wear my blue jeans,
And dance to rock and roll.

VET

When I grow up I'll be a Vet,
And if your pet is ill,
Just bring it to my clinic,
And I'll cure it with some pills.

If you have a monkey,
That cannot climb up trees,
Then I'll put up a ladder,
And he'll go up with ease.

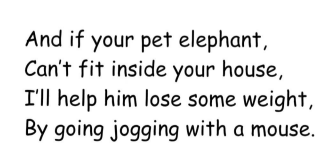

And if your pet elephant,
Can't fit inside your house,
I'll help him lose some weight,
By going jogging with a mouse.

And if your pet crocodile,
Has a tooth that's causing pain,
I'll wrap it up with string,
Tied to the Bangkok train.

Oh, I'd truly love to be a Vet,
But it's only that,
They don't allow pets,
In our high-rise flat!

CHEF

When I grow up I'll be a chef,
In my own restaurant,
I'll have a giant kitchen,
And cook anything I want.

I'll boil up some soup,
A bowl of hot Tom Yum,
And just one little taste,
Will put fire in your tongue.

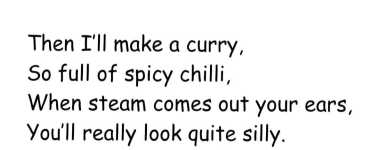

Then I'll make a curry,
So full of spicy chilli,
When steam comes out your ears,
You'll really look quite silly.

And finally, for dessert,
Mango and sticky rice,
Topped with coconut milk,
Will taste so sweet and nice.

Oh, I'd like to be a chef,
In a 3-foot hat,
But with all that food,
I might get too fat.

FISHERMAN

Those other jobs have problems,
As you can plainly see,
There's really only one thing,
That's suitable for me.

And that's to be a fisherman,
Living out at sea,
I wouldn't have to dress up nice,
With no one watching me.

I'd sail upon the waves,
Going anywhere I please,
And never lose my way,
'Cos there are no roads at sea.

I'd never catch a cold,
And I'd never cough or wheeze,
For there's no smog and dust,
Out in the fresh sea breeze.

And I wouldn't have to worry,
About getting frozen ears,
For I'd grow my hair quite long,
And have a woolly beard.

And I could keep a pet,
A parrot, dog or cat,
And need not be afraid of heights,
Because the sea is flat!

I'd eat a lot of fish,
And have a nice flat tummy,
And when it got too hot,
I'd go swimming when it's sunny.

And if I needed money,
I'd just toss out my net,
And haul in tons of fish,
With hardly any sweat.

Yes, I'll surely be a fisherman,
When I'm fully grown,
I'll sail my ship far away,
...If my mum lets me leave home ...

<u>WORD LIST</u>

If you have never visited Thailand then some of the words in this book may be new to you. If so, just look for the words on the list below and you will find their meanings.

<u>WORD</u>	<u>MEANING</u>
Tuk-tuk	Three-wheeled taxi.
Soi	Small road or lane.
Chiang Mai	A city in the North of Thailand.
Phuket	An island in the South of Thailand.
Bangkok	The Capital City, in Central Thailand.
Mangoes	A tasty Thai fruit, green on the outside and yellow inside.
Mangosteen	A Thai fruit, purple on the outside, white inside.
Durian	A Thai fruit with a very strong smell! On the outside, it is spiky and hard like a football.
Rambutan	A juicy, white, Thai fruit, red and "hairy" on the outside.
Temple	Where monks live and Thai people go to pray.
Baht	Thai money.
Tom yum	A hot and spicy Thai soup.
Sticky rice	A type of Thai rice. When it is cooked, the grains stick together.

Meet the Author

Janice is an Australian who has lived in Bangkok for almost 20 years. She is married and has three children. She is a graduate of The University of Melbourne and holds a Math/Science teaching degree as well as a PhD in Chemistry. Before coming to Thailand she worked as a Research Scientist in the USA. After settling down in Bangkok, she taught English at a Thai school for several years before publishing her first book, The Little Blue Tuk-tuk, in 2000. She is now a full-time writer.

Other books by the same author

The Little Blue Tuk-tuk by Janice Santikarn, illustrated by Sukit Tanmankong, Thai Watana Panich Press, Bangkok, 2000. Reprinted Sirivatana Interprint Public Co. Ltd., Bangkok, 2006

Nawin Saves the Elephants by Janice Santikarn, illustrated by Rong Prapasanobon, Thai Watana Panich Press, Bangkok, 2000

ABC of Thailand by Janice Santikarn, illustrated by Janice Santikarn and Toni Skinner, Rung Silp Printing, Bangkok, 2001. Reprinted Sirivatana Interprint Public Co. Ltd., Bangkok, 2003

Koko the Monkey: Lost in Bangkok by Janice Santikarn, illustrated by Prateep Paisarnnan, Sirivatana Interprint Public Co. Ltd., Bangkok, 2002. Reprinted 2005

The Brave Little Tuk-tuk by Janice Santikarn, illustrated by Sukit Tanmankong, Sirivatana Interprint Public Co. Ltd., Bangkok, 2004